MICE ON ICE

There are at least 10 differences in these two pictures. How many can you find?

CROWD PLEASERS

What's everybody looking at? Match the people with the events they are watching.

PEOPLE

A.

B.

C.

D.

E.

EVENTS

1.

2.

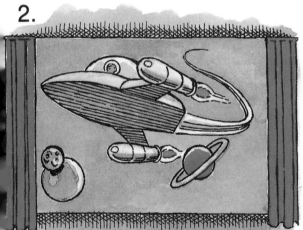

3.

4.

5.

Answer on page 47.

WOW!

Watch out for words that begin with the wiggly letter W!
How many can you find?

Illustrated by John Nez

Answer on page 47.

EASY AS ABC

If you know your ABCs, you can break this code. Below every letter in this riddle write the letter that comes *before* it in the alphabet. If you see B, write A. If you see C, write B, and so forth.

A B C D E F G H I J K L M N O P Q R S T U V W X Y Z

Riddle:

I̲ S̲T̲A̲Y̲ _ _ _ _ _   _ _ _
J   T U B Z   X J U I   Z P V

_ _ _   _ _ _ _ _ _ _ _   _ _ _ .
B M M   U I S P V H I   U I F   E B Z.

_ _ _ _   _ _ _   _ _ _ _   _ _ _ _
X I F O   U I F   T V O   H P F T   E P X O

_ _ _   _ _ _ _ .
J H P   B X B Z.

_ _ _ _   _ _   _ _ ?
X I B U   B N   J

Answer:

_ _ _ _   _ _ _ _ _
Z P V S   T I B E P X

Illustrated by John Nez

Answer on page 47.

PUZZLEMANIA **7**

PICTURE CROSSWORD

Look at the pictures and write the words in the spaces across and down.

ACROSS

1.

2.

4.

6.

8.

9.

11.

13.

15.

16.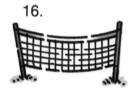

18.

19.

20.

DOWN

1.

2.

3.

4.

5.

6.

7.

10.

11.

12.

14.

17.

Illustrated by Dennis Panek

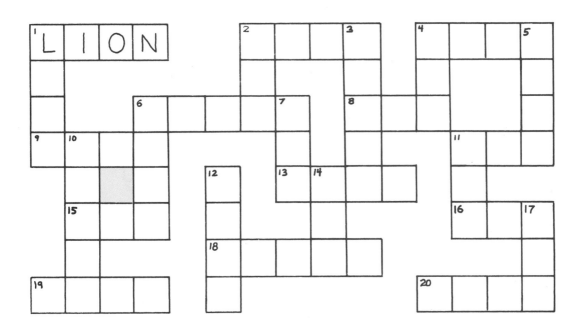

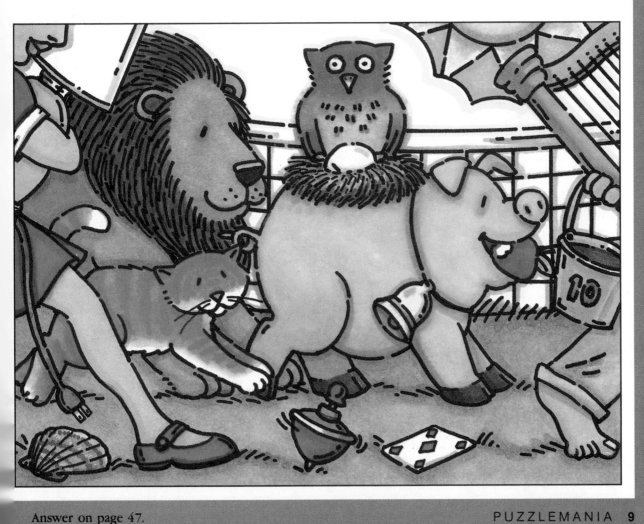

MINUS MAZE

To find your way through this maze, subtract the first pair of numbers (6 – 1). Draw a line to the answer (5), then move to the next pair of numbers and do the same. Answers may be to the left, right, up or down.

Answer on page 47.

LOOK AROUND

Twenty round things are hidden in this puzzle.
How many can you find? Look up, down, across, backward, and diagonally.

PANCAKE   KNOB   COIL   BEAD

QUARTER

CIRCLE   PLATE

SAUCER

SPOT

```
        R L D
      I S I C B O E
    P C O N N R T A Q        HOOP
    A C I G V A U R U
    K N O B R L C B E A D
    S C H S P C E E E R O
    H A L O P Z L Y L T T
    K U U O O E E L E
    E C C B P T R R R
    R U E N O I O
        E R T
```

ZERO

DOT

TIRE

HALO

TUBE

CUP   BRACELET   COIN
                                          REEL

RING

Answer on page 47.

GET A LOAD OF THIS!

Charlie is confused. Sometimes people do not mean exactly what they say. "Get a load of this!" does not mean "Fill your wheelbarrow with this!" It really means "Look at this!" So, "get a load of" some sayings below. Help Charlie find the right meaning for each.

1. When Charlie's father says "hold your horses!", what should Charlie do?

   a. Buy some horses and tie them up.

   b. Ride a merry-go-round.

   c. Stop what he is doing.

2. What does Charlie's grandmother mean when she says he is "cute as a bug's ear?"

   a. He looks like a fly's ear.

   b. He looks very cute.

   c. He doesn't hear very well.

3. If Charlie's friend is going to "hit the hay," what is he about to do?

   a. Go to sleep.

   b. Sit on a bale of hay.

   c. Tackle a scarecrow.

4. Charlie's parents went on a cruise. They said it took a few days to "get their sea legs." What did they mean?

   a. They weren't used to the steadily rocking boat.

   b. They ordered crab legs for dinner and had to wait a long time.

   c. After a few days, their legs turned into salt water.

Don't blow your top, Charlie!

5. Charlie's friend says: "Don't blow your top!" What doesn't she want him to do?

   a. Rip his shirt.

   b. Get angry.

   c. Break the nose of his model airplane.

6. When Charlie decided to read a 500-page book in one hour, his sister said that he shouldn't "bite off more than he can chew." What does his sister think?

   a. Charlie plans to do more than he really can.

   b. Charlie should not eat when he reads.

   c. Charlie's book is made of chocolate.

7. Charlie's mom said he should put his money in the bank to "build a nest egg". What does she mean?

   a. Charlie's money will be made into a bird nest.

   b. Someday Charlie will have a lot of money in the bank.

   c. Birds will eat Charlie's money and lay green eggs.

This will help build a nice nest egg for you.

Illustrated by John Nez

Answer on page 47.

PATCHWORK PUZZLER

Find these squares in the quilt below.

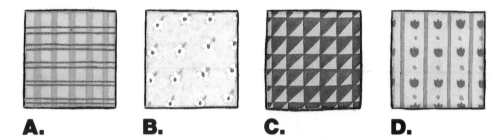

A. **B.** **C.** **D.**

Illustrated by Jennifer Skopp

Answer on page 48.

STOP, LOOK, AND LIST

Under each category list one thing that begins with each letter. For example, one vegetable that begins with P is potato. See if you can name another.

Vegetables

P _____

C _____

L _____

O _____

S _____

Sea Creatures

P _____

C _____

L _____

O _____

S _____

Bodies of Water

P _____

C _____

L _____

O _____

S _____

Answer on page 48.

Illustrated by Doug Taylor

WHICH CORNER?

Here's how Holly gets home from school. Follow the directions carefully and draw an X on each street corner where she stops. Then try taking the Neighborhood Quiz.
(Hint: Remember that "right" and "left" depend on the direction you're heading at the time.)

1. Holly's school is at the corner of West and Maple. Holly walks out the front door and turns right on Maple Street.

2. At the end of the block she turns left.

3. She goes three blocks and stops at the corner to visit her friend Mrs. Thistle.

4. Then she turns right and walks two blocks.

5. She stops at the corner to mail a letter, turns right, and goes two more blocks.

6. She turns left, goes one block, and stops to look for the puppy who lives on the corner.

7. Then she turns left onto her street. Her house is the second one on the left.

Neighborhood Quiz

1. Mrs. Thistle lives on the corner of _____
   and _____ .

2. The mailbox is on the corner of _____
   and _____ .

3. The puppy lives on the corner of _____
   and _____ .

4. Holly lives on the corner of _____
   and _____ .

5. What color is Holly's house?

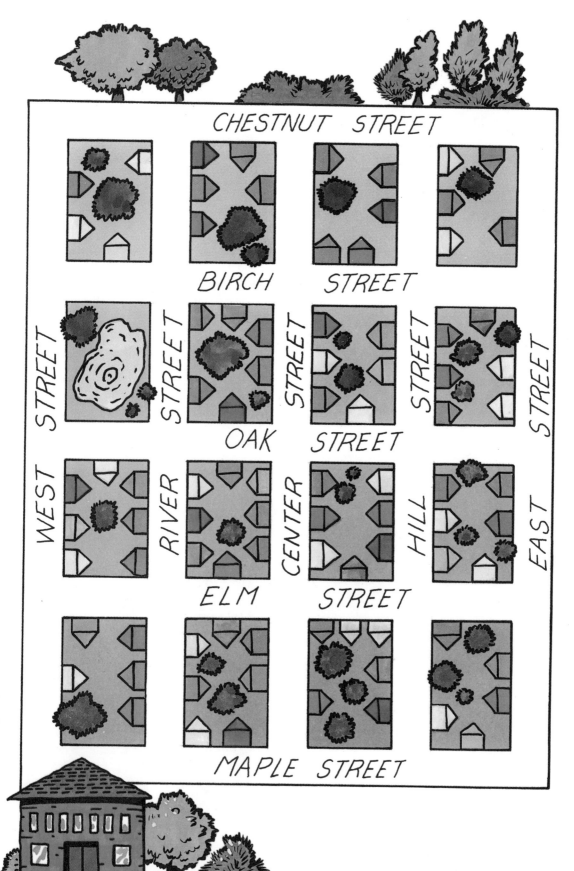

CHESTNUT STREET

BIRCH STREET

OAK STREET

ELM STREET

MAPLE STREET

WEST STREET

RIVER STREET

CENTER STREET

HILL STREET

EAST STREET

Answer on page 48.

DOT MAGIC

Connect the dots to find out what
David likes to play after school.

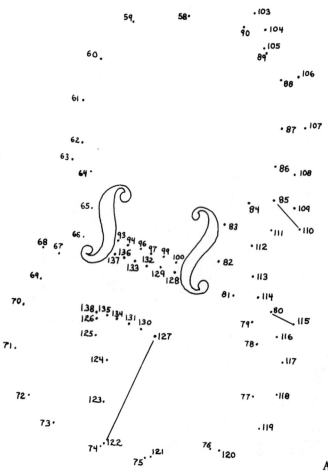

Answer on page 48.

Illustrated by Deanna Goodenough

THE CLUTTERED CLOSET

Take a long look at this picture. Try to remember everything you see in Carly's closet. Then turn the page, and try to answer some questions about it without looking back.

Illustrated by Judith Hunt

DON'T READ THIS UNTIL YOU HAVE LOOKED AT "The Cluttered Closet— Part 1" ON PAGE 19.

THE CLUTTERED CLOSET

Part 2

Can you answer these questions about the cluttered closet you saw? Don't peek!

1. Did you see a soccer ball?
2. Did Carly have a clown mask or a cat mask?
3. How many balloons did you see?
4. Was there a cushion on the chair?
5. Which hung on the door, the baseball hat or the sombrero?
6. Was the bowling ball on the top shelf?
7. How many stuffed bears did you see?
8. Did Carly's clothes hang on one side of her closet or on both sides?

Answer on page 48.

SOMETHING IN COMMON

These objects have something in common. What is it?

Illustrated by Judith Hunt

Answer on page 48.

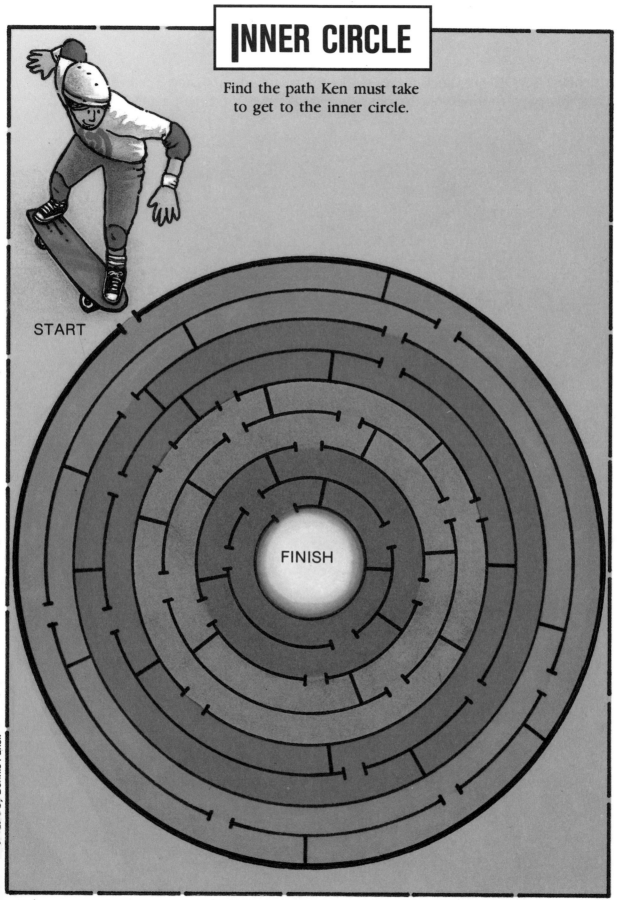

INNER CIRCLE

Find the path Ken must take
to get to the inner circle.

START

FINISH

IT'S ABOUT TIME!

Clock 1 says 10:30. Clock E says 4:30, which is six hours later. For every timepiece on this page, find one on the next page that shows the time exactly six hours later.

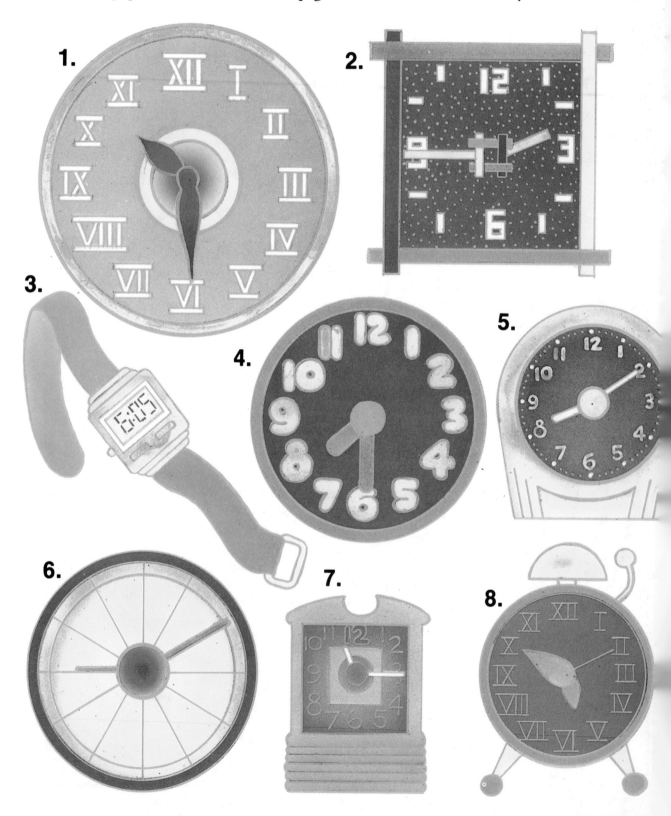

1.

2.

3.

4.

5.

6.

7.

8.

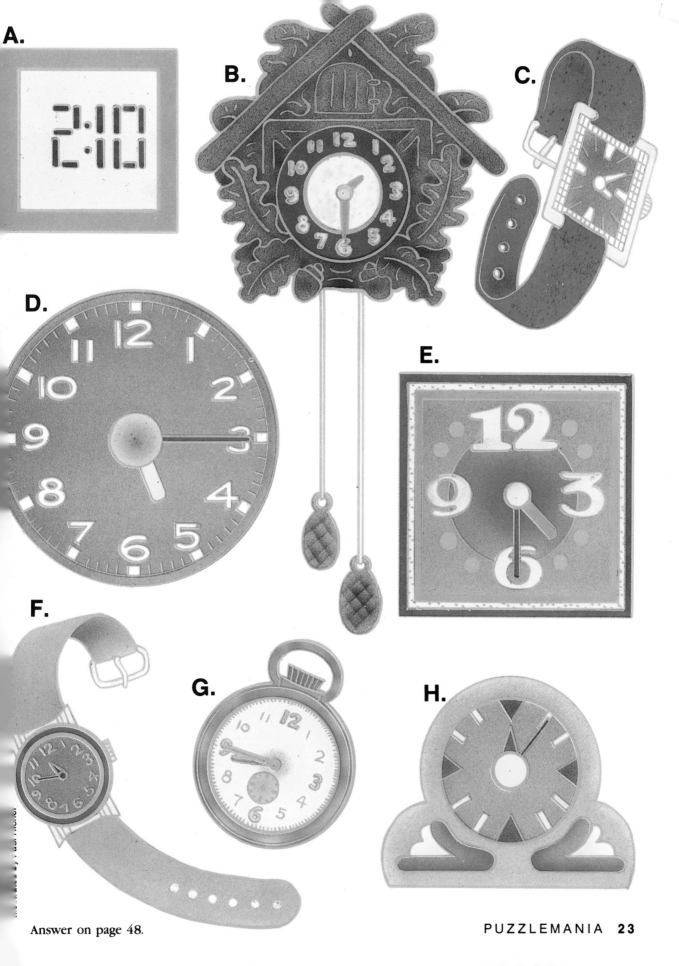

A.

B.

C.

D.

E.

F.

G.

H.

Answer on page 48.

ROW, ROW, ROW

Each kitten has something in common with the two others in the same row. All three kittens in the top row across have spots. Look at the other rows across, down, and diagonally. What's the same about each row of three?

Illustrated by Judith Hunt

Answer on page 48.

THREEN GUMB GARDENER

Daisy, the Green Thumb Gardener, grows perfect petunias. But she cannot make a sentence without mixing up the first sounds of some words. For example, her helper's first job is supposed to read "find a sunny patch of ground." Can you un-mix Daisy's note, so her helper knows his other jobs?

Jelper's Hobs

1. **Sind** a **funny gratch** of **pound.**
2. Plow the soil and add **fant plood.**
3. **Dake** the **rirt** to help **rick** out **pocks.**
4. **Rant** a **plow** of **sower fleeds.**
5. **Sover** the **ceeds** with dirt.
6. Every day, **live** the seeds **gots** of **wesh frater.** Be sure the **nose hozzle ginkles sprently,** or the **drowers** may **floop.**
7. **Sope** for **hunshine.**
8. **Wull** out the **peeds,** when they **bet** too **gig.**
9. Enjoy the beautiful **gower flarden.**
10. **Bake** a **touquet mome** to your **hother.**

Answer on page 49.

Illustrated by John Nez

HIDDEN PICTURES

There are at least 12 objects hidden in this picture.
How many can you find?

26

27

WRONG-WAY CROQUET

How many things can you
find wrong in this picture?

Illustrated by Marc Nadel

INSTANT PICTURE

What's hidden on this page? To find out, fill in every
section that contains two dots.

Answer on page 49.

JIGSAW MATCH

Which of these is the missing puzzle piece?

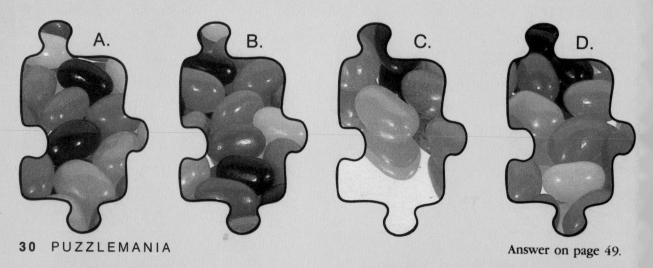

A.

B.

C.

D.

Answer on page 49.

WORLD SEARCH

Find the names of the countries, past and present, hidden in the letters below. Look up, down, across, diagonally, and backward.

AUSTRALIA
AUSTRIA
BELGIUM
CANADA
CHILE
CHINA
CUBA
ENGLAND

GERMANY
GHANA
GUINEA
HAITI
HOLLAND
ICELAND
INDIA
IRAN

IRAQ
ITALY
JAPAN
LIBYA
NEPAL
NIGERIA
PERU

SOVIET UNION
SPAIN
SWITZERLAND
UNITED STATES
VENEZUELA
VIETNAM
YUGOSLAVIA
ZAIRE

```
Y C Y U G O S L A V I A H I A
N I H M U I G L E B U D A N U
A I T I Z A I R E S N F I D S
M D N A L R E Z T I W S T I T
R E T I L E H R D A E O I A R
E R B O W Y A S I T N V D S I
G Y Q P I L A T A U L I G R A
A A A G I E O T D E A E H I L
L I R A N A S Y A T P T A C M
P R I I T D I D N B E U N E A
O E U D E R S P A I N N A L N
S G R T C U B A C T U I O A T
Y I I U R V D N A L L O H N E
E N G L A N D E T E P N R D I
U J A P A N A L E U Z E N E V
```

Illustrated by Bill Basso

IS IT TRUE?

Which sentences are true? Which are false?

True **False**

____ ____ 1. Leap year comes every ten years.

____ ____ 2. Babe Ruth was a famous football player.

____ ____ 3. Dates grow on palm trees.

____ ____ 4. Paper comes from wood.

____ ____ 5. Vienna is a large city in Australia.

____ ____ 6. Bats are blind.

____ ____ 7. Elephants are afraid of mice.

____ ____ 8. It never rains in the desert.

____ ____ 9. Leather comes from plants.

____ ____ 10. Sponges are animals.

____ ____ 11. A jonquil is a kind of flower.

____ ____ 12. Hawaii is the smallest state in the U.S.

Illustrated by Jerry Zimmerman

Answer on page 49.

ZOO MYSTERY

Maria went to the Petting Zoo. She saw a goat, a duckling, and a wrinkly baby elephant. But there was one animal she liked best of all. What do you suppose it was? Use your imagination and draw the animal.

WHAT'S IN A WORD?

Using the letters in SCARECROW you can make RACE, COW, and many other words. Can you find at least 20 words in SCARECROW?

_____

_____

_____

_____

_____

_____

_____

_____

_____

_____

_____

_____

_____

_____

_____

_____

_____

_____

Answer on page 49.

THE NINETEENTH HOLE

Stan's golf ball missed the eighteenth hole and disappeared. Stan's best friend, Old Blue, knows where it went. Help Old Blue find his way through the tunnel.

Illustrated by Judith Hunt

Answer on page 49.

DISTANT RELATIVES

Both objects in each pair have a part with the same name. For example, both a clock and a person have a face. Can you find the common part for each pair?

1.

2.

3.

4.

5.

6.

7.

Answer on page 49.

TRASH TO TREASURE

Place these words in the spaces below to finish the poem.

best	goes	president
can	gold	sizes
~~Clash~~	guest	spaghetti
compliment	knows	surprises
confetti	old	trash
dinner	pan	winner

My friend Claudia C l a s h

Never has any __ __ __ __ __ .

Anything broken and __ __ __ ,

To Claudia, looks like pure __ __ __ __ .

Her right shoe's a used coffee __ __ __ .

Her left shoe's an old frying __ __ __ .

Her belt is cold __ __ __ __ __ __ __ __ __ .

Her hair sparkles with __ __ __ __ __ __ __ __ .

When Claudia comes to __ __ __ __ __ __ ,

The host is always the __ __ __ __ __ __ .

Everybody __ __ __ __ __

Everywhere Claudia __ __ __ __

She brings trashy __ __ __ __ __ __ __ __ __

In all shapes and __ __ __ __ __ .

While visiting the __ __ __ __ __ __ __ __ __

She got a special __ __ __ __ __ __ __ __ __ __ .

"Lemon peel ties are the __ __ __ __ .

Claudia Clash,

   you're my favorite __ __ __ __ __ !"

Answer on page 50.

THANKS, I'LL JUST HAVE TOAST

The cooks at the Daybreak Diner were bored with breakfast. One day they decided to scramble the menu instead of the eggs. Use this code to see what new recipes they cooked up.

Code:

A = O
B = K
C = R
D = T
E = U
F = P
G = H
H = G
I = Y
J = V
K = B
L = N
M = S
N = L
O = A
P = F
Q = X
R = C
S = M
T = D
U = E
V = J
W = Z
X = Q
Y = I
Z = W

MENU

1. _ _ _ _ _ _ _   _ _ _ _
   D A O M D U T   S Y N B

2. _ _ _ _ _ _   _ _ _ _ _
   F O L R O B U   V E Y R U

3. _ _ _ _ _ _   _ _ _ _ _ _ _ _
   A C O L H U   F A D O D A U M

4. _ _ _ _   _ _ _ _ _ _ _   _ _ _ _ _ _ _
   G O M G   K C A Z L U T   S E P P Y L M

5. _ _ _ _ _   _ _ _ _   _ _ _ _ _
   K O R A L   Z Y D G   M I C E F

6. _ _ _ _ _   _ _ _ _ _ _ _ _ _ _ _
   P C Y U T   K N E U K U C C Y U M

PICTURE MIXER

Copy these mixed-up squares in the spaces on the next page to put this picture back together. The letters and numbers tell you where each square belongs. The first one, A-3, has been done for you.

A-3 A-2 A-1 A-4
B-1 B-3 B-4 B-2
C-2 C-3 C-1 C-4
D-1 D-2 D-4 D-3

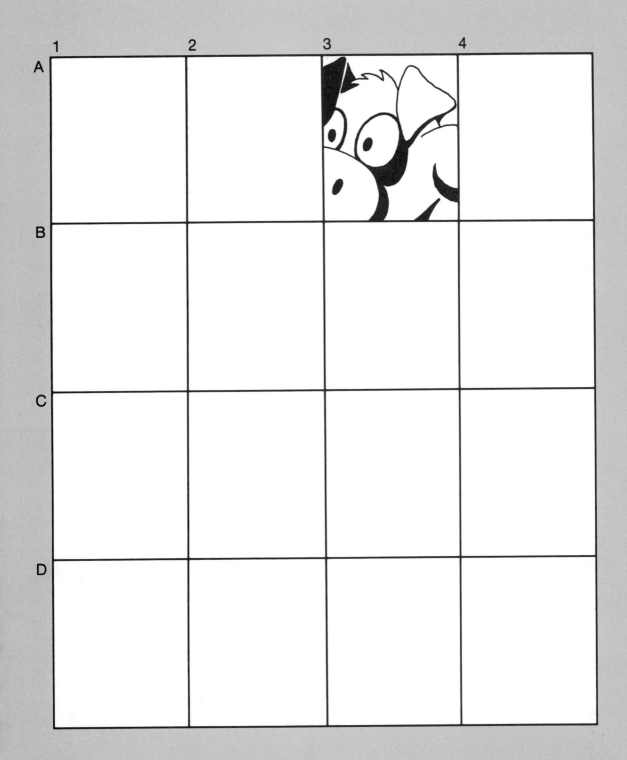

FALL INTO PLACE

Number the pictures to show what happened first, second, and so on as summer turned into fall.

Illustrated by John Nez

Answer on page 50.

DOT PLAY

Karen's uncle runs a big machine that helps build skyscrapers. Connect the dots to find out what it looks like.

Answer on page 50.

"IN" WORDS

Every word in this puzzle contains the letters "IN" Use the clues to help you fill in the IN words across and down.

ACROSS

1. Pane of glass
3. A breeze is a soft gust of _____
7. Cloth or paper item for mealtime spills
8. Use your brain
10. Close and open both eyes quickly
11. Big, toothy smile
15. Cut, bruise, sprain or broken bone
16. Dime, nickel, or penny
17. Person who runs a train
20. Liquid from a pen
22. Hotel
23. Place where a beard grows
25. Song performer
27. Country whose capital is Madrid
29. Slender
30. Very small

DOWN

1. Season between autumn and spring
2. Pig noise
3. Opposite of lose
4. Beverage
5. Turn in circles like a top
6. A bird flaps this to fly
9. Sixty seconds
12. Jewelry for your finger
13. Number after eight
14. Red-breasted bird
18. There are twelve _____ in a foot
19. Evergreen tree
21. Man who wears a crown
24. Close and open one eye quickly
25. Basin with faucets and a drain
26. Water that falls from clouds
28. Straight, sharp metal fastener

CYCLE CHUCKLE

Why can't a bicycle stand up?
To find the answer, fill in the names of the
bicycle parts shown in this picture. Then move
the numbered letters into the answer spaces.

A. _ _ _ _ _
       8

B. _ _ _ _ _
       3

C. _ _ _ _
     7

D. _ _ _ _
     5

E. _ _ _ _ _
   2

_ _ _ _ _
     4

F. _ _ _ _
         1

G. _ _ _ _ _ _ _ _ _
                     6

Answer: Because it is

_ _ _ _ _ _ _ _
1 2 3 4 5 6 7 8

Illustrated by John Nez

ANSWERS

CROWD PLEASERS (pages 4-5)

A. 4   B. 1   C. 5
D. 2   E. 3

WOW! (page 6)

waffle
wagon
wall
walkway
walnut
walrus
washing machine
wastebasket
water
watermelon
water ski
waves
weasel
weathervane
west
whale
wheel
wheelbarrow
whiskers
wig
windmill
window
wings
wink
wishbone
wishing well
woodpecker
worm
wreath
wrench

EASY AS ABC (page 7)

I stay with you
all through the day.
When the sun goes down
I go away.
What am I?
Answer: Your shadow.

PICTURE CROSSWORD (pages 8-9)

MINUS MAZE (page 10)

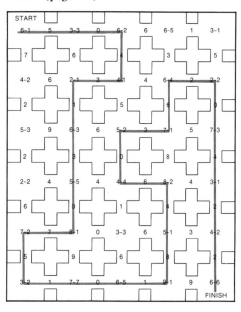

LOOK AROUND (page 11)

GET A LOAD OF THIS! (pages 12-13)

1. C. Stop what he is doing.
2. B. He looks very cute.
3. A. Go to sleep.
4. A. They weren't used to the steadily rocking boat.
5. B. Get angry.
6. A. He plans to do more than he really can.
7. B. Someday he will have a lot of money in the bank.

PATCHWORK PUZZLER (page 14)

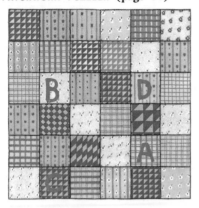

STOP, LOOK, AND LIST (page 15)

Here are our answers. You may have found others.

Vegetables	Sea Creatures
Pea	Porpoise
Carrot	Clam
Lettuce	Lobster
Onion	Octopus
Spinach	Shark

Bodies of Water
Pond
Creek
Lake
Ocean
Stream

WHICH CORNER? (pages 16-17)

1. Mrs. Thistle lives on the corner of River Street and Birch Street.
2. The mail box is on the corner of Birch Street and Hill Street.
3. The puppy lives on the corner of Elm Street and East Street.
4. Holly lives on the corner of Oak Street and East Street.
5. Holly's house is gray.

DOT MAGIC (page 18)

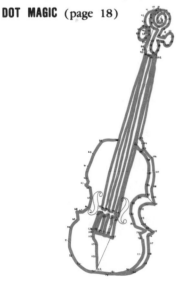

THE CLUTTERED CLOSET (page 20)

1. Yes, there was a soccer ball.
2. Carly had a cat mask.
3. There were two balloons.
4. There was a cushion on the chair.
5. The baseball hat hung on the door.
6. No, the bowling ball was not on the shelf.
7. There were three stuffed bears.
8. Carly's clothes hung only on one side of the closet.

SOMETHING IN COMMON (page 20)

They all need wind to work.

INNER CIRCLE (page 21)

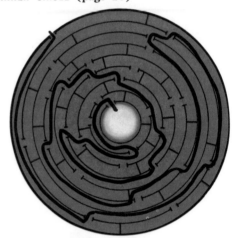

IT'S ABOUT TIME! (page 22)

1.	10:30	E.	4:30
2.	2:45	G.	8:45
3.	6:05	H.	12:05
4.	7:30	B.	1:30
5.	8:10	A.	2:10
6.	9:10	C.	3:10
7.	11:15	D.	5:15
8.	5:50	F.	11:50

ROW, ROW, ROW (page 24)

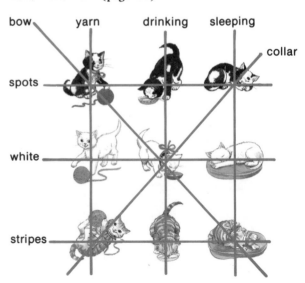

THREEN GUMB GARDENER (page 25)

1. **Find** a **sunny patch** of **ground.**
2. Plow the soil and add **plant food.**
3. **Rake** the **dirt** to help **pick out rocks.**
4. **Plant** a **row** of **flower seeds.**
5. **Cover** the **seeds** with dirt.
6. Every day, **give** the seeds **lots** of **fresh water.** Be sure the **hose nozzle sprinkles gently,** or the **flowers** may **droop.**
7. **Hope** for **sunshine.**
8. **Pull** out the **weeds,** when they **get** too **big.**
9. Enjoy the beautiful **flower garden.**
10. **Take** a **bouquet home** to your **mother.**

INSTANT PICTURE (page 29)

JIGSAW MATCH (page 30)

B

WORLD SEARCH (page 31)

IS IT TRUE? (page 32)

1. False. Leap Year actually comes every **four** years.
2. False. Babe Ruth was a famous **baseball** player, not a football player.
3. True. Dates **do** grow on palm trees.
4. True. Paper **does** comes from wood.
5. False. Vienna is a large city in **Austria,** not Australia.
6. False. Bats are **not** blind. However, they do not see well.
7. False. Elephants are **not** really afraid of mice.
8. False. It **does** sometimes rain in the desert.
9. False. Leather comes from **animals,** not plants.
10. True. Sponges really **are** animals.
11. True. A jonquil **is** a kind of flower.
12. False. Hawaii is **not** the smallest state in the United States, Rhode Island is.

WHAT'S IN A WORD? (page 34)

Here are twenty words we found in SCARECROW. You may have found others. Many more words can be made by adding "s" to most of these words. For example, COW becomes COWS.

ace	oar
are	race
car	rear
care	roar
case	saw
core	scare
cow	score
crew	soar
crow	wear
ear	worse

THE NINETEENTH HOLE (page 35)

DISTANT RELATIVES (pages 36-37)

1. Trunk
2. Ears
3. Stories
4. Foot
5. Keys (and pedals)
6. Needles
7. Teeth

TRASH TO TREASURE (page 38)

My Friend Claudia **Clash**
Never has any **trash.**

Anything broken and **old,**
To Claudia, looks like pure **gold.**

Her right shoe's a used coffee **can.**
Her left shoe's an old frying **pan.**

Her belt is cold **spaghetti.**
Her hair sparkles with **confetti.**

When Claudia comes to **dinner,**
The host is always the **winner.**

Everybody **knows**
Everywhere Claudia **goes**

She brings trashy **surprises**
In all shapes and **sizes.**

While visiting the **president**
She got a special **compliment.**

"Lemon peel ties are the **best.**
Claudia Clash, you're my favorite **guest!**"

THANKS, I'LL JUST HAVE TOAST (page 39)

1. Toasted milk
2. Pancake juice
3. Orange potatoes
4. Hash browned muffins
5. Bacon with syrup
6. Fried blueberries

PICTURE MIXER (pages 40-41)

FALL INTO PLACE (page 42)

4	5
2	6
3	1

DOT PLAY (page 43)

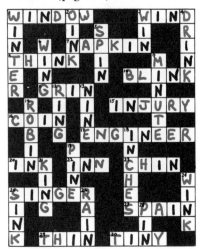

"IN" WORDS (page 44)

WINDOW   WIND
NAPKIN
THINK   BLINK
GRIN
INJURY
COIN
ENGINEER
INK   INN   CHIN
SINGER
SPAIN
THIN   TINY

CYCLE CHUCKLE (page 46)

A. Pedal
B. Spoke
C. Gear
D. Tire
E. Water bottle
F. Seat
G. Handlebar

Because it is **two-tired** (too tired).